# Thank you ...

... for buying this copy of Handwriting Today Book 1.

Handwriting Today Book 1 can be used to improve the appearance of your handwriting, whether you are 8 or 80. We will guide you with our step by step approach covering:

...the correct way to hold the pen and the paper or exercise book

...sitting comfortably and appropriately for writing

...techniques for joining letters

...capital letters and lower case letters

When you have completed this book you may like to advance your writing further by using our next handwriting book:

## Handwriting Today Book 2

Handwriting Today Book 2 revises the letter structures and join formations but also features:

...punctuation marks and their use

...numerals and the pound sign

...writing for pleasure

...writing formal correspondence

D0347597

Important things to remember include:

Making sure that your table or desk is not cluttered - you can't write well
where you have piles of books, pens, biscuits, drinks and other odd items.

GIVE YOURSELF SPACE.

Sitting where there is good light.  The room in the picture actually has a window
at both ends, so our writer is not causing too much shadow over her work.

Finding a chair and table of appropriate heights.  Are you comfortable, without
having to reach up to the table?

Holding your paper still.  Our writer in the picture is holding the paper with her
left hand to ensure that the paper doesn't move as she writes.

It may seem strange but we are going to start by looking at the letter c.

This is because the structure of the letter c makes a good starting point for several other letters of the alphabet.

1. Start writing here.

2. Write in an anti-clockwise direction.

It is essential that you follow these instructions for the letter c. You **must** start at the top and you **must** write in an anti-clockwise direction.

Now try some for yourself:

CC

Let's get smaller:

C C C

...and smaller:

c c c

Most exercise books and sheets of lined paper have line spacings of 8 millimetres:

You need to write your letters so that they sit on the bottom line and are about half as tall as the total space. We have drawn an extra faint line to help you:

c c c

Now try without the extra line. Make sure you keep the letters the same size:

c c c

If you are left handed:

You should take care not to press too hard when you are writing, as left handed people have to 'push' the pen across the paper rather than 'pull' it as right handed people do.

You may need to take special care when choosing a pen. If you use a fountain pen, did you know that you can buy nibs which are especially designed for left handed people? Special nibs are not needed with most other types of pen.

You should try to hold your paper at an angle so that you can see what you have written. If not you will find that your hand covers over the writing and sometimes makes it smudge.

Your handwriting can be as good as anybody's!

## More letters

Remember that the structure of the letter c makes a good starting point for several other letters of the alphabet. We are now going to look at the letter o. This starts in exactly the same place as a letter c, but unlike the c it finishes in the same place as it started.

1. Start writing here.

2. Write in an anti-clockwise direction.

1. Start and finish here.

2. Write in an anti-clockwise direction.

Now try some for yourself.
Make sure that each letter sits exactly on the line.

OO

OOO

ooo

Now let's look at letter a. This is made in the same way as the c and the o. When you reach the finish point of the o, continue upwards by a small amount, then come down to the line and finish with a small sloping upstroke:

aaa

aaa

We are now going to try writing the word 'cocoa'. Don't try to join yet - that's coming soon. Do try to keep your letters on the bottom line and leave gaps between words:

cocoa cocoa cocoa

You may be used to holding your pen in a different way,
but you might like to try this way:

Hold the pen near the point but not so close that your fingers get inky.

Rest the pen on your second finger.

Grip the pen between your thumb and your index finger.  Hold it tightly
but comfortably.

Keep the pen at a slope.

Sit so that you can see each letter as you write.

Don't forget the basic shape of the letter c, then the formation of the letters o and a.
Letter d is very similar to the letter a but obviously the 'stick' is taller.
Because letter d is taller than the other letters we call it an ascender.

Now try some for yourself.
Make sure that each letter sits exactly on the line.

ddd

d d d

The letter g is made in a similar way to the c and the o. When you reach the finish point of the o, continue upwards by a small amount, then come down, going through the line and ending with a curl in a clockwise direction. Because letter g goes below the line we call it a descender.

ggg

ggg

We have two new words to practise. The lines are shown as they would appear in most exercise books. Notice how high the d goes and how far below the line that the g goes.

cod dog

# Choosing the pen

Choosing the right pen is extremely important. Pens come in an enormous variety of shapes and sizes. Once you have developed your handwriting skills you may wish to experiment with different nibs to achieve special effects. For now, we suggest using a pen with a fine point. You may also like to consider these ideas:

Make sure that the pen is comfortable to hold. If it is too thin or too fat it can cause your fingers to ache.

Select a pen which 'feels right' in your hand. Some people like pens with a very smooth finish while other people find that these pens slip or become sticky with sweat!

Find a pen which allows the ink to flow freely. You do not want to have to press hard on the paper. Neither do you want a pen which produces blobs of ink, as some ballpoints do.

If choosing a cartridge pen, make sure that the cartridges are easy to change. You don't want cartridges which leak all over your fingers.

Letter e is created using the same anti-clockwise movement which we have used in all the letters so far, but we start this letter in a different place:

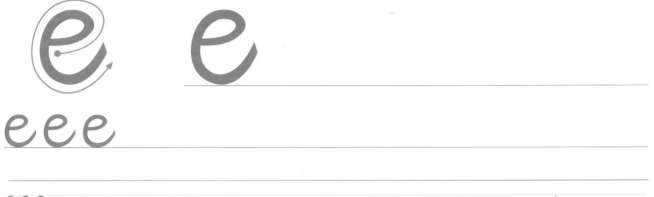

*e e e*

*e e e*

Letter q is a rather simpler form of the letter g.  Having created the basic shape of a letter a, we move down through the line, then give a very small upstroke to complete the letter:

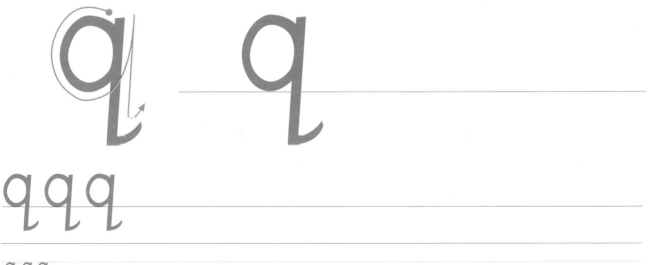

*q q q*

*q q q*

Letter s is formed by starting with our familiar anti-clockwise movement then curling quickly round to a clockwise movement:

Try copying this pattern of letters s and c.  Make sure that the s is the height of the c.

*SC SC*

*SC SC SC*

The words we have written so far are: cocoa dog cod
Now that we have practised the letter e we will add one more word: code
First, let's look at the word 'cocoa' in joined writing:

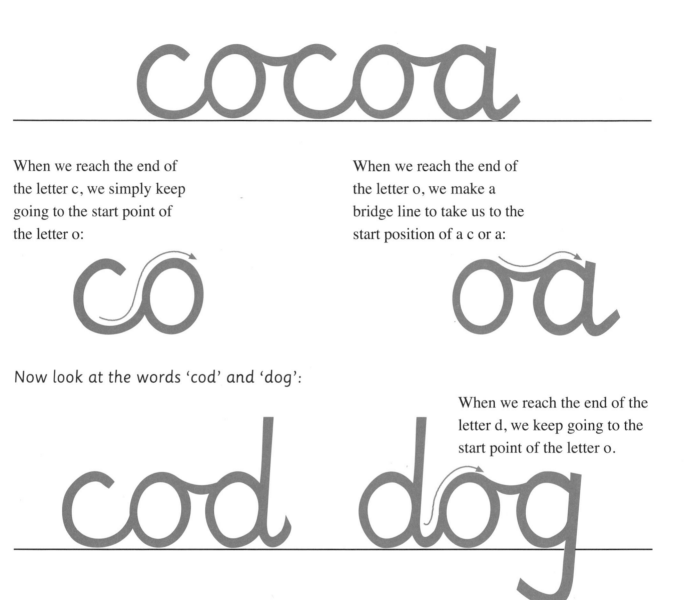

When we reach the end of the letter c, we simply keep going to the start point of the letter o:

When we reach the end of the letter o, we make a bridge line to take us to the start position of a c or a:

Now look at the words 'cod' and 'dog':

When we reach the end of the letter d, we keep going to the start point of the letter o.

Look carefully at the joins in the word 'code':

We normally write a letter e like this:

To join to the e we change it to look like this:

When we reach the end of the letter d, we flow into the letter e.

Try writing the word 'cocoa' in joined writing. Remember to keep all the letters the same height. Make sure that all the letters sit neatly on the line. Keep a clear gap between the words.

cocoa cocoa

cocoa cocoa cocoa
cocoa cocoa cocoa
cocoa cocoa cocoa
cocoa cocoa cocoa

Now try the words 'cod' and 'dog':

cod dog

cod dog
cod dog
cod dog
cod dog

Notice that we make sure that the tail of the g does not crash into the stick of the d.

When you practise the word 'code', remember that it has three different types of join: the **slope** from the c to the o, the **bridge** from the o to the d and the **flow** from the d to the e. Notice that this flow is at the same angle as the slope from the c to the o.

code

code code
code code
code code
code code

The formation of the letter s can change slightly when we make a join to it.
Look carefully at this word:

New shape s

Normal shape s

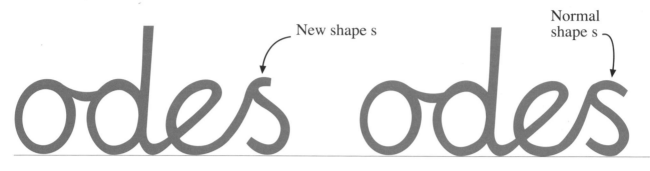

Which letter s do you prefer? The choice is yours.

Here is another choice: some people like to join from a letter s; some people prefer not to. Look at the word seed, written in two ways. Decide which type of letter s you wish to use, joined or unjoined.

We can now look at another choice, this time with a letter g:

To join or not to join? The choice is yours.

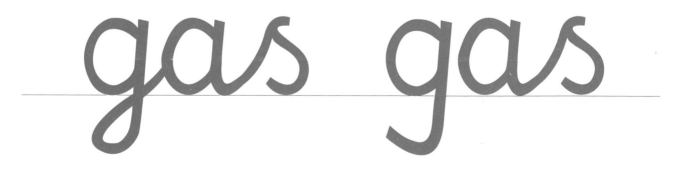

Look at the use of letter s and letter g in these words, comparing the joined methods with the unjoined. Which do you prefer?

Try writing the word 'gas' in joined writing. Choose whether to join from the g or not. You could try both ways to see which you prefer.

*gas gas*

gas gas
gas gas
gas gas

Now try the word 'seeds'. Decide whether you would like to join from the letter s.

*seeds seeds*

seeds
seeds
seeds

Practise each of the words below. Be careful with letter sizes.
We have chosen to join from the letters s and g. You can make a choice as to what looks best in your own handwriting.

as
cages
cogs
goose

Now practise the words again, writing as quickly as you can. Are they still tidy?

as
cages
cogs
goose

The letter l is the same height as the letter d but is formed differently.
It is, of course, a very simple letter to draw. The letter i is similar but shorter and, obviously, we need to put a dot over it. The dot should be drawn last of all. Sometimes you will write a complete word, then return to the i to draw the dot.

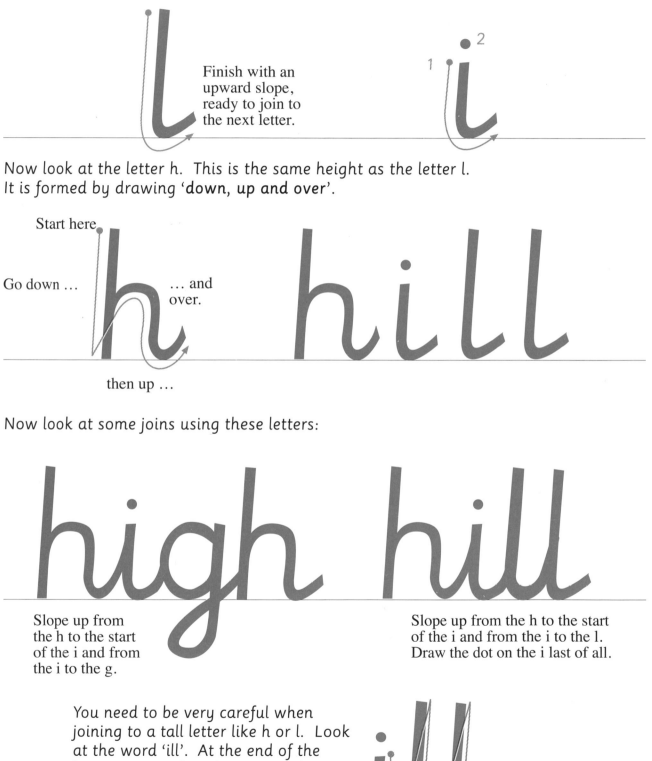

Finish with an upward slope, ready to join to the next letter.

Now look at the letter h. This is the same height as the letter l.
It is formed by drawing '**down, up and over**'.

Start here
Go down …
… and over.
then up …

Now look at some joins using these letters:

Slope up from the h to the start of the i and from the i to the g.

Slope up from the h to the start of the i and from the i to the l. Draw the dot on the i last of all.

You need to be very careful when joining to a tall letter like h or l. Look at the word 'ill'. At the end of the letter i we need to slope up to the starting point of the letter l, then draw down exactly along the same line:

# Practising with letters l, i and h

Try writing the word 'hill' in joined writing.  Slope up from the h to the i, from the i to the first l and from the first l to the second l:

*hill hill*

Notice how tall the letters h and l are compared to the letter i.  Making sure that your letters are the correct height can make a huge difference to your handwriting.

*hill hill hill*
*hill*
*hill*

Here is a short phrase.  Write it several times.
Try to make each phrase look better than the one before.

*a high hill*
*a high hill*

Practise each of the words below.  Be careful with letter sizes.
We have chosen to join from the letters s and g.  You can make a choice as to what looks best in your own handwriting.

*shall*
*heel*
*legs*
*goal*

Now practise the words again, writing as quickly as you can.  Are they still tidy?

*shall*
*heel*
*legs*
*goal*

You need to be very careful when joining to tall letters.
Let's look again at the join from a letter i to a letter l:

You have a choice:

You can flow from the
letter i right up to the top
of the letter l …

… or, if you find it easier, you
can briefly take your pen off the
paper at the end of the slope of
the letter i, then draw the
letter l so that it looks like it is
joined to the letter i:

Now let's look at joining from a letter o to a letter l.  As you will remember, we normally
use a bridge join from the top of a letter o to the next letter.  When joining from
letter o to a tall letter, we make a sloping join:

Here is the
normal bridge
join from a letter
o to a letter a:.

This is the sloping
join which we use
from a letter o
to a tall letter.

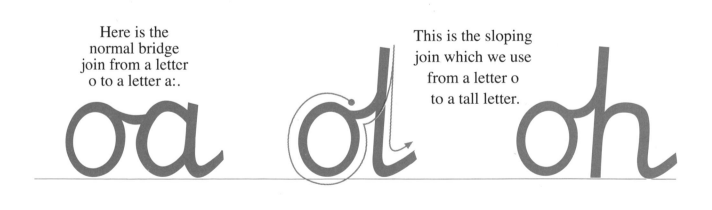

oh so old
oh ill oil chill leech each heel heal deal glade glide

# Practising joining to tall letters

Practise joining a letter i to a letter l.  Try both of the ways shown on page 16.
First try joining where you keep the pen flowing from the slope of the letter i right up
to the starting point of the letter l:

*il*

*il*

Now try the method where you take your pen off at the end of the slope from the
letter i, then draw the letter l to look like it's joined to the letter i:

*il*

*il*

Decide which method you prefer, then always stick to it.

Let's practise joining from a letter o to tall letters like l and h:

*ol oh*

Try writing this short phrase several times:

*oh so old*

These words give you practice in joining to tall letters:

*deal*

*oil*

*chill*

*each*

*glide*

Letter n is very similar to letter h. It is formed by drawing '**down, up and over**'.

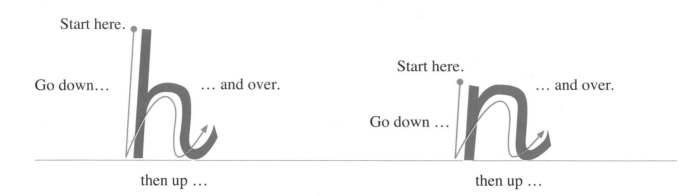

Letter m is very similar to letter n. It is also formed by drawing '**down, up and over**' but then the '**up and over**' is repeated:

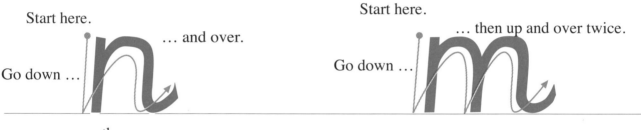

Now is a good time to remember letter sizes. Let's look at all the letters we've practised:

c o a d g e q s h i l m n

These letters can be split into groups:

… ordinary small letters:

c o a e s i n m

… tall letters, called ascenders:

d h l

… letters which go below the line, called descenders:

g q

Try writing the word 'mean' in joined writing.
Make sure that all the letters are exactly the same height,
fitting neatly between the lines provided.

*mean*

mean

mean

Practise each of the words below. The ascender letter l should be taller than the small letters in the words. The smaller letters should all be exactly the same height. This time there are no blue lines to guide you. You will need to judge sizes carefully.

lean

clean

lame

nail

Look carefully again at a letter g. The **bowl** of the g should be sitting exactly on the line, as the other letters do. The **tail** of the g should go through the line.

*game* or *game*

Practise each of the words below.

game

main

dance

sing

dingle

cinema

inside

Letter r is formed in a similar way to a letter n by going '**down, up and over**' but obviously we don't go right over.  Look at these letters n and r:

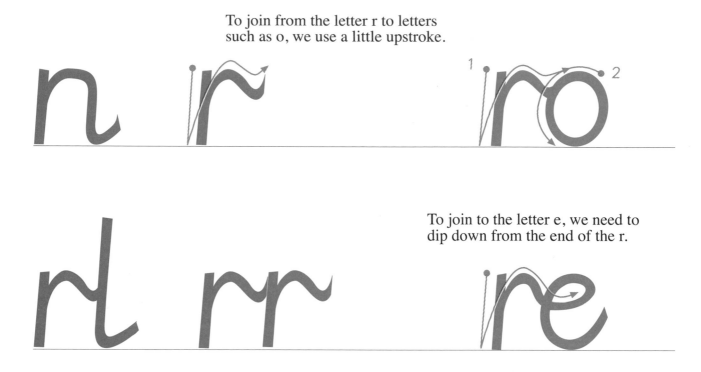

To join from the letter r to letters such as o, we use a little upstroke.

To join to the letter e, we need to dip down from the end of the r.

Letter t is formed from the top like a letter l.  It is not as tall as a letter l.  We draw the cross-line on the t **after** we have finished the word we are writing.  If there is a double t, we draw the line through both letters together.

To join from the letter t, we simply draw an upstroke.

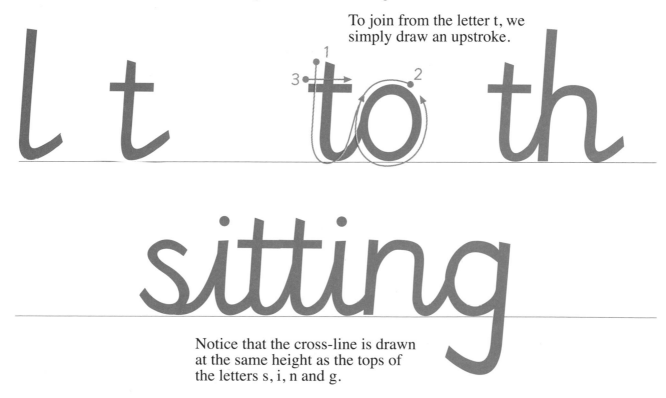

Notice that the cross-line is drawn at the same height as the tops of the letters s, i, n and g.

# Practising with letters r and t

Try writing the word 'rate' in joined writing.
Make sure that all the letters are exactly the same height, except for the letter t which is slightly taller than the others. Draw the cross-line on the t last of all.

*rate*

rate
rate

Practise each of the words below.

girl
girls
art
starring

These words contain a common letter pattern which has a letter t at the end:

tight
light
might
right

Practise each of the words below. Notice the word which features the double t.

date
letter
seat

Now try these words, writing as quickly as you can. Can you keep your writing tidy?

staring
sitting
distance

Letter b is created by starting at the top, like a letter h.  We then come down, up and over, completing the letter with a bowl shape:

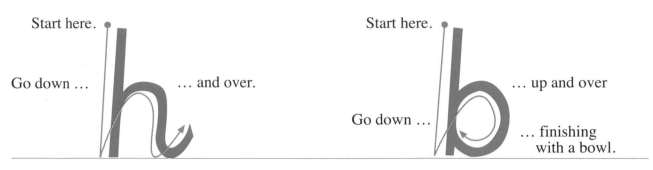

Start here.

Go down …                                    … and over.

then up …

Start here.

Go down …                                    … up and over

… finishing
with a bowl.

Look at these two versions of the letter b:

*nibs nibs*

Some people choose to join from a letter b, some people choose not to.
Which do you prefer?

Letter k is also formed from the top like a letter l.  When we reach the line, we move upwards just as we would for a letter b.  We go up and over, but then turn in sharply to make a loop which meets the stick.  We then slope downwards, before finishing with an upstroke:

*k    k*

Look at the use of a letter k in two words of this phrase:

*keen on milk*

## Practising with letters b and k

Try writing the word 'beak' in joined writing.
The letters e and a should be exactly the same height.  The ascending letters b and k
should be the same height as each other and clearly taller than the letters a and e.

# beak

beak

beak

Practise each of the words below.

milk

globe

seek

able

Practise writing this short sentence.  Write it several times, trying to get faster but
keeping your writing very tidy.

He is keen on baking cakes.

TIME CHALLENGE
Time yourself for thirty seconds . Write the word 'break' as many times as
you can but keep it tidy!  You should be able to write the word 'break',
neatly, about ten times.

break

Letter p is very similar to a letter b.  We start at the top of the stick, draw down through the line, draw up the same line, then loop over to make the bowl.

Start here.

Go down …

… and over to make the bowl.

then up …

Start here.

Go down …

… and over to make the bowl.

then up …

Compare these two words:

sips   sips

In the first version we are not joining to or from the letter s and we are not joining from the letter p.  In the second version we are joining all the letters.
Which do you prefer?

Now is a good time to practise joining from top-joiners, like letters o and r, to a letter e:

To join from the o to the e we need to dip down to the starting point of the letter e:

oe

We join from a letter r to a letter e in a similar way:

re

Look at a normal join from a letter o, using a **bridge** to the letter m:

Compare this to the join to the letter e, where we use a **dip**:

tomatoes

Try writing the word 'peach' in joined writing.
The letters e, a and c should be exactly the same height. The ascending letter h should be taller than e, a and c but notice that the 'lump' on the h is the same height as these letters. The 'stick' of the letter p must go down through the line and the 'bowl' of the letter p should be the same height as the letters e, a and c.

*peach*

*peach*

*peach*

Practise each of the words below.

*limp*

*deep*

*ripple*

*deeper*

Now practise these words, which include joining to a letter e from a 'top-joiner':

*repeat*

*toes*

*reap*

*potatoes*

 TIME CHALLENGE
Time yourself writing the word 'potatoes'. Keeping your writing tidy, how long does it take you to write 'potatoes' ten times?

*potatoes*

Letter ƒ is a very unusual letter because it is both an ascender and a descender. Not only that, its cross-line is drawn straight after drawing its basic shape rather than at the end of a word as we would with the letter t. This cross-line can then be used to join to the next letter - because of its height, the cross-line creates a join like a top-joiner such as letter o or letter r.

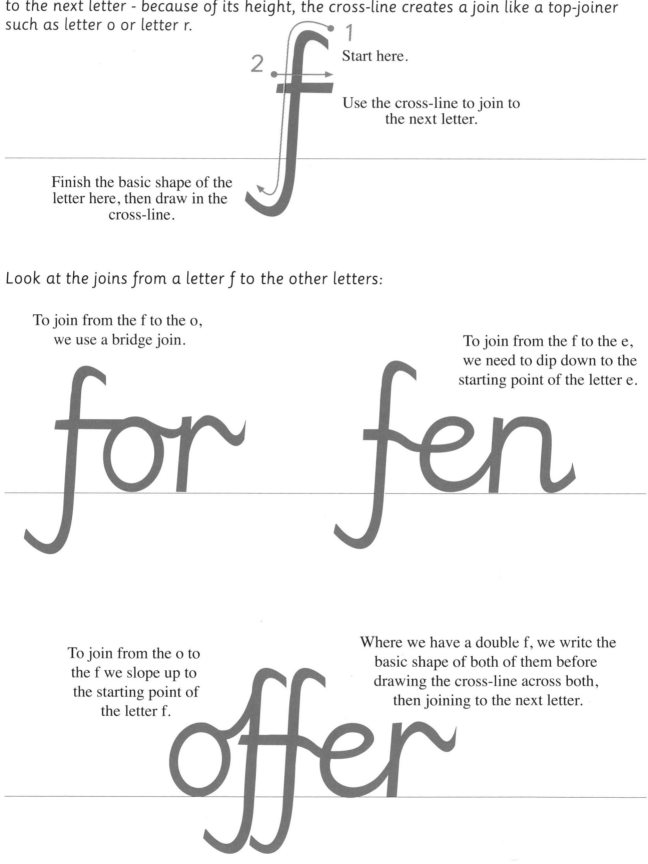

1 Start here.

2

Use the cross-line to join to the next letter.

Finish the basic shape of the letter here, then draw in the cross-line.

Look at the joins from a letter ƒ to the other letters:

To join from the f to the o, we use a bridge join.

for

To join from the f to the e, we need to dip down to the starting point of the letter e.

fen

To join from the o to the f we slope up to the starting point of the letter f.

Where we have a double f, we write the basic shape of both of them before drawing the cross-line across both, then joining to the next letter.

offer

Try writing the word 'friend' in joined writing.
The letters f and d should be the same height but, of course, the letter f continues below the line. The letters r, i, e and n should be the same height as the bowl of the d.

*friend*

friend

friend

Practise each of the words below.

fire

freedom

fantastic

Now practise these words, which include joining to a letter e as well as some doubles:

fen

offer

for

feeling

TIME CHALLENGE
How many times can you write the word 'certificate' in one minute, while keeping your writing neat?

certificate

# Introducing letters j and y

So many people have trouble with the letter j.  It is actually a very simple letter to draw. These are the rules for a letter j:

Start at the top of the letter, making sure that the top is the same height as a letter a.
Draw down through the line, finishing with an 'umbrella handle' tail, like a letter g.
Draw the dot in afterwards.
We can choose whether to join from a j.

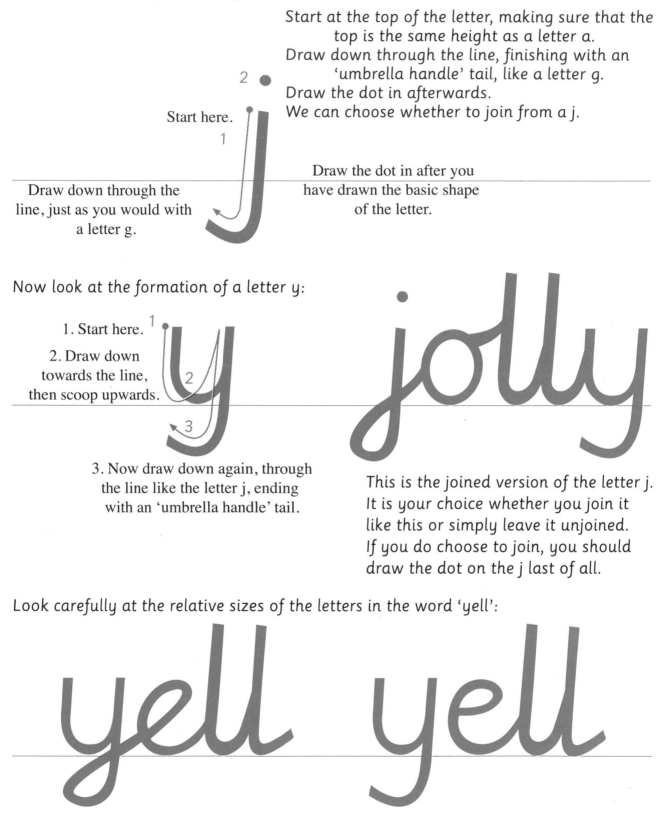

2 ●

Start here.

1

Draw down through the line, just as you would with a letter g.

Draw the dot in after you have drawn the basic shape of the letter.

Now look at the formation of a letter y:

1. Start here. 1 ●

2. Draw down towards the line, then scoop upwards.

2

3

3. Now draw down again, through the line like the letter j, ending with an 'umbrella handle' tail.

This is the joined version of the letter j. It is your choice whether you join it like this or simply leave it unjoined. If you do choose to join, you should draw the dot on the j last of all.

Look carefully at the relative sizes of the letters in the word 'yell':

Do you prefer the joined or the unjoined version of the letter y in the word 'yell'?
If you choose to use the joined version of the letter y, you ought to choose to use the joined version of the letter j in order to keep your writing consistent.

Try writing the letters j and y alternately.  Both letters start at the same height and both go below the line to the same depth, but the letter j has a dot added to make its overall height taller than the letter y.

jy jy

jy jy
jelly

Notice that when you write the word 'jelly' on the lower line, the ascenders may crash into the descenders from the line above.  To avoid this you need to position the words on the lower line to miss the descenders from above.   Now practise these words:

yes
jingle
majority

Now try the same words again, without the blue guideline.
Can you keep your writing tidy?

yes
jingle
majority

Practise writing the sentence below several times.  Concentrate on the sizes of the letters, making sure that your ascenders are high enough and that your descenders are low enough.  After writing the sentence on the lines provided, try writing it at the bottom of the page without lines at all.  Can you keep your writing tidy?

The jolly major is in the jeep eating jelly.

We have already practised letter q on page 9 but we have not been able to use it within any words because we haven't yet looked at letter u.

1.Start here.

2. Draw down towards the line then scoop upwards, just like a letter y.

3. Now draw down again, stopping at the line and ending with a joining upstroke.

Letter u is quite a straightforward letter to deal with.  Letters before it join on to it easily and it is also easy to join from it because of its upstroke:

about

Letter q is always followed by a letter u.
You have a choice whether you want to join the two letters together:

qu          qu

Some people think that it is tidier not to join the q to the u.

Which do you prefer: joined or unjoined?

The choice is yours.

qu          or          qu

Practise writing q and u together.  You can try out the joined and unjoined methods and decide which you prefer.

qu qu

qu qu
queen

Practise each of these words:

antique
jaguar
junior

Let's have a look at a capital letter q so that we can begin a sentence with 'Quickly':

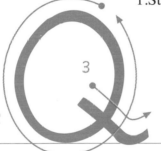

1. Start here.

2. Draw round completely to make the shape of a letter o.

3. Draw the tail across the bottom right sector of the basic letter shape.

Practise writing some capitals, then try the sentence below.

Q

Q

Quickly, mend the umbrella using glue.

Letters v and w are extremely similar to each other:

Start here.

Finish with a very short stroke which will be used as a bridge to join to another letter.

We join from the v to the e by dipping from the end stroke of the letter v:

We join from the w to the a using a bridge join:

Now look at the formations of the capital versions:

The capital letter v is very simple.

You have two choices with the capital letter w:

Where the centre peak is full height:

or

Where the centre peak is lower than the two arms:

The choice is yours.

Practise writing the word 'with'. Remember to complete the word before returning to put the dot on the letter i and to put the cross on the letter t.

with

with

with

Practise each of the words below.

very

over

tomorrow

low, lower, lowest

Write the sentence below several times. Try to get faster each time you write the sentence but make sure you keep your writing tidy. Take particular care to keep your letters the correct size. Make sure that the ascenders are tall enough and that the descenders go far enough below the line.

We saw Vera, walking very quickly.

TIME CHALLENGE
Time yourself writing the sentence below. How quickly can you write it while keeping your writing tidy? Make a second attempt to see if you can get any faster.

Welcome Victor when he arrives.

Letters x and z are unlike any other letters.
Letter x is made by drawing two separate lines.
We can join to the letter x but we can't join from it.

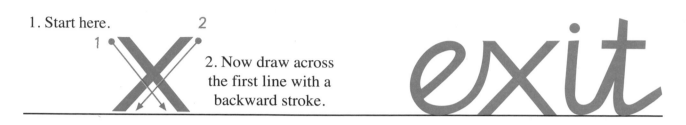

1. Start here.

2. Now draw across the first line with a backward stroke.

Letter z is formed by one continuous line:

You can join **to** a letter z from a preceding letter, such as the letter a in the word 'amaze'. You have a choice whether to join **from** the letter z.

| Some people choose to leave the letter z unjoined: | Others choose to join using an upstroke: |

Which do you prefer?

The choice is yours.

The capital versions of letters x and z are simply larger versions of the lower case letters:

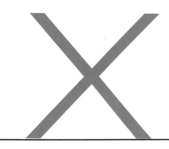

Practise writing the word 'exit'. Remember to join the letter x from the e but do not join the x to the i. Make sure that you keep the two parts of the word close together so that it does not look like two words: exit not ex it.

## exit

exit

exit

Practise each of the following words below.

fox

fax

razor

crazy

Write the sentence below several times. Try to get faster each time you write the sentence but make sure you keep your writing tidy. Our sentence takes up a full length of the line - yours may take more than a whole line

There was amazing excitement over the craziness of the zebra

TIME CHALLENGE
Time your self writing the sentence below. How quickly can you write it while keeping your writing tidy? Make a second attempt to see if you can get any faster.

The fox left the zoo through the main exit.

We have already practised some of the capital letters. Over the next few pages we will practise writing all of them. Look carefully at the formation of the capital letters from A to L before practising them on page 37.

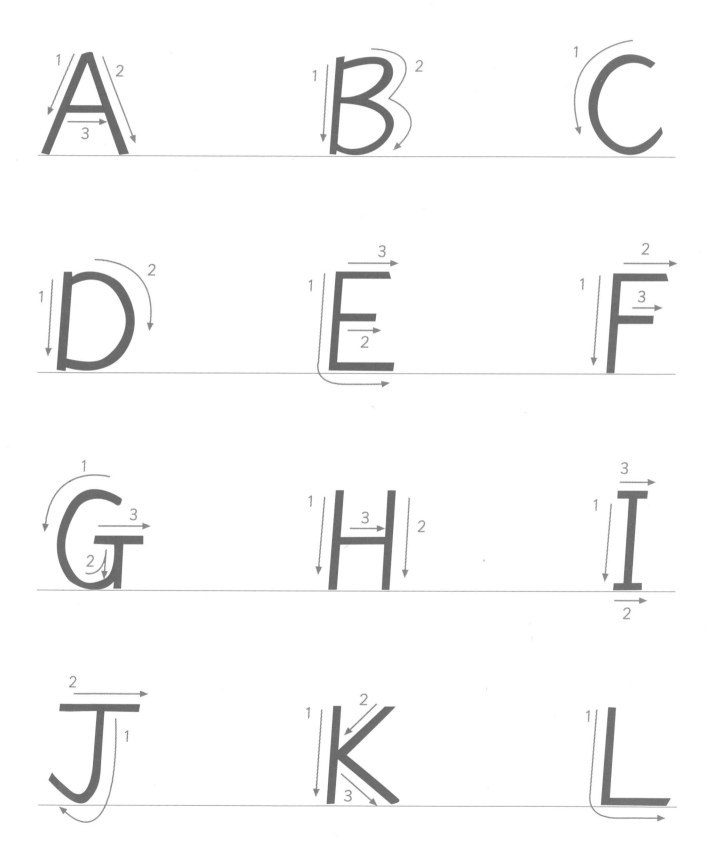

Practise writing each capital letter together with the lower case version of the same letter. Look at the similarities and differences between the letters.

Aa  Aa
Bb  Bb
Cc  Cc
Dd  Dd
Ee  Ee
Ff  Ff
Gg  Gg
Hh  Hh
Ii  Ii
Jj  Jj
Kk  Kk
Ll  Ll

Now try writing the names of these places. Make sure that your capital letters are as tall as the ascenders. Do not join the capital letter to the letter which follows it.

America
Bermuda
Canada
Denmark
England
Fiji
Guyana
Hungary
India
Japan
Korea
Laos

Look carefully at the capital letters from M to Z, before practising them on page 39.

Practise writing each capital letter together with the lower case versions.

Mm

Nn

Oo

Pp

Qq

Rr

Ss

Tt

Uu

Vv

Ww

Xx

Yy

Zz

Now try writing the names of these places:

Malaysia

Nigeria

Oman

Peru

Qatar

Rwanda

Switzerland

Turkey

Uruguay

Venezuela

Western Sahara

Xai-Xai

Yemen

Zaire

## Presenting your work neatly

By working through this book you have learnt the basic letter formations and joins. These will enable you to write tidily and quickly. There are a few simple rules which you will need to apply at any time that you are writing:

Make sure that you are sitting comfortably, that your desk is not cluttered, that you have good light to work by and that you are holding your paper still.

Choose a pen which you are comfortable with and hold it correctly ...
... you might like to refer back to pages 6 and 8.

If you are left handed, look back at our tips on page 4.

Be very careful to keep your letters the right size:

All of these letters
are equal in height:

a c e i m n o r s u v w x z

The ascenders are taller
than the letters above:

b d f h k l t

The descenders all
come below the line:

f g j p q y

Now look at all the letters together, comparing their sizes:

a b c d e f g h i j k l m n o p q r s t u v w x y z

Be careful to keep a clear gap between your words ...

I went for a walk today     I went for a walk today

... but don't make the gaps too wide!

You may like to write on plain paper instead of lined paper. On the inside of the back cover we have provided a line-guide, with appropriate margins.
You can fasten your A4 size paper to the line-guide using paper-clips.

To make further improvements to your writing and presentation, there's lots more practice in **Handwriting Today Book 2**. We hope that you have enjoyed Book 1.